This book was created for people who feel overwhelmed and need a distraction.

#YESIHAVEANXIETY
Deal. With. It.

To all my new friends,

Thank you so much from the bottom of my heart for all your support with the launch of my new book! I feel the love and cannot wait to connect with you and see your creations on TikTok. I feel so lucky to have connected with so many people out there experiencing anxiety like me. I no longer feel alone and misunderstood, and I hope you feel the same when you see all the people in the comments going through similar struggles pulling together through TikTok and creativity. We've got this!!

~~BE CREATIVE and HAVE FUN~~ – all the extra supplies I use in my videos come from things around the house or Dollar Tree. This is your book – you make the rules on what your page looks like. The prompts are there for an example. Be sure to tag me in all your posts. As a team, we can bring awareness to anxiety sufferers like you and me.

You are the first to know – I am already working on my second book! If you are interested in receiving an email when it launches, please go to http://yesihaveanxiety.square.site/ and enter you email under my picture 😊

Always remember to ignore the haters - .."Be who you are and say what you feel because those that mind don't matter and those who matter don't mind. "– Dr. Suess

Love your new friend,

Nicole

TikTok - @nicoleeandevan

WIN A FREE BOOK!
Winners drawn WEEKLY!

Follow these steps to be entered into a drawing to win a free book!

1. Post a video of you filling out your book using the hashtag #YesIHaveAnxiety

2. Tag us in your video!

3. Comment 3 friends in our most recent video!

Paint Each Box with Nail Polish

Color This Whole Page
Yellow, then Write an
Inspiring Quote

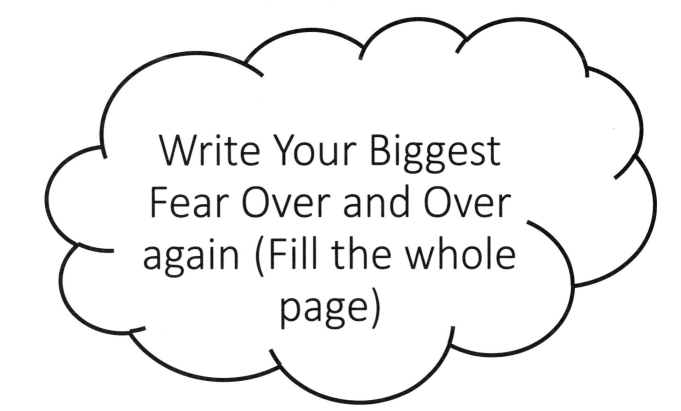

Make His Teeth White

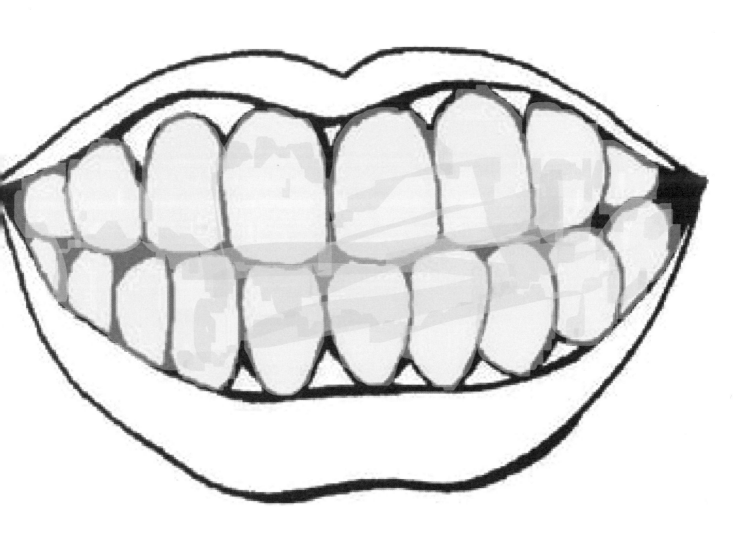

Cut Out Pictures Of a Magazine and Glue Them Here to Make a Collage (Fill the Whole Page, But Don't Cover These Words!)

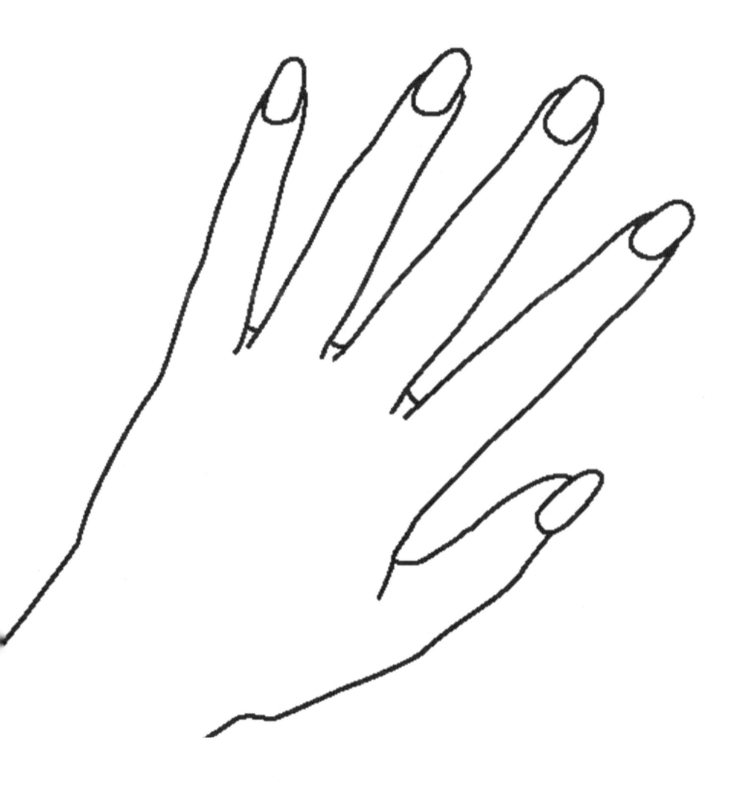

Paint
Her
Nails

Put Stickers
All Over This
Page

Color Inside the Lines with Different Shades of Your Favorite Color

Glue Flowers
to This Page,
Fake or Real

Decorate the
Mask with
Wrapping Paper

Cut a Piece of Fabric and Glue it in the Square (Preferably Very Textured)

Make the Clouds Puffy

(Cotton Balls, Paint, Feathers, ANYTHING)

Put Skittles all
Over the Rainbow
(Real or Fake)

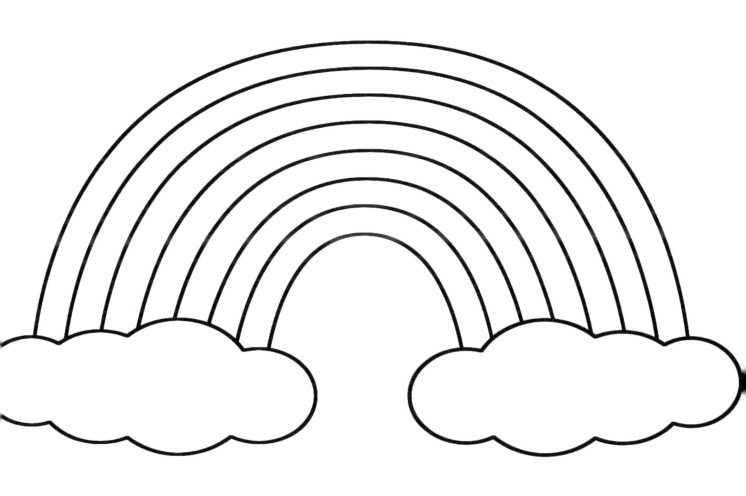

Make These Donuts Ugly

On a Separate Piece of Paper, Write Down all Your Feelings. Tear the Piece of Paper Up and Place the Scraps Here

Draw What
You Ate Today

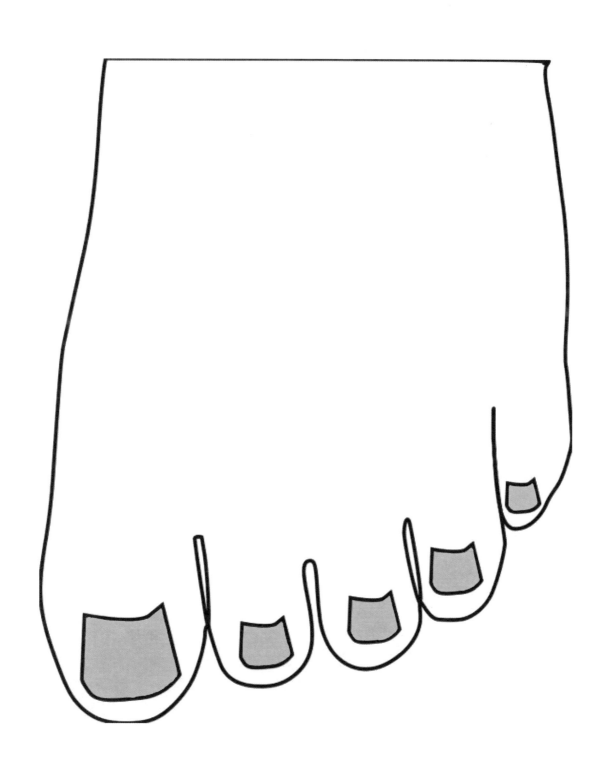

Decorate the Christmas Tree (Be Creative!)

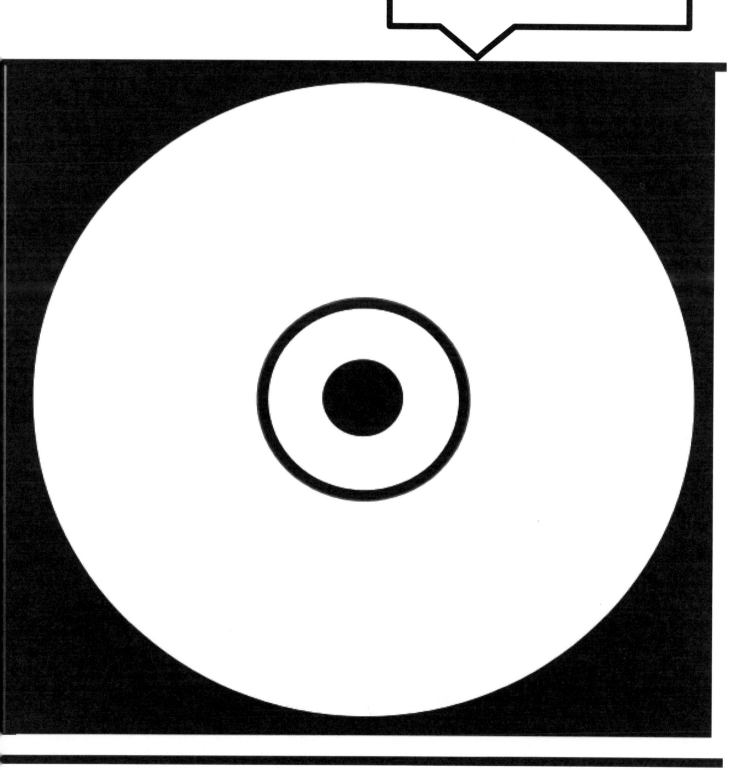

Create a Puzzle!
(Color these Pieces to
Make your Own
Puzzle, Cut Them Out
and Glue Them on
the Next Page, Do not
Glue Them In Order)

Show
Me
Your
Puzzle!

Create Something From This!

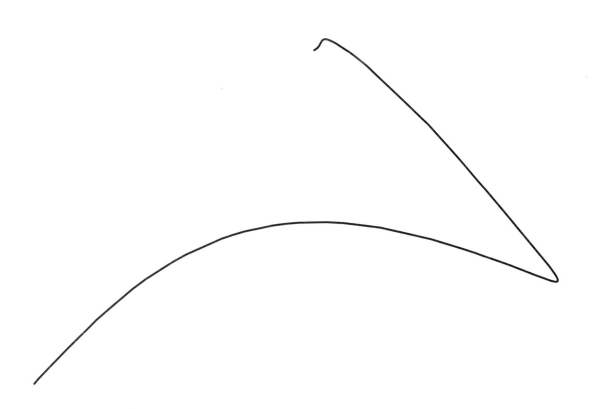

Fill This Page
with Colorful
Circles, Don't
Let them
Overlap!

Make
These
Donuts
Pretty

Color This Page Your Favorite Color, Then Write Everything that Makes You Happy.

Draw Your Idea Of Happiness

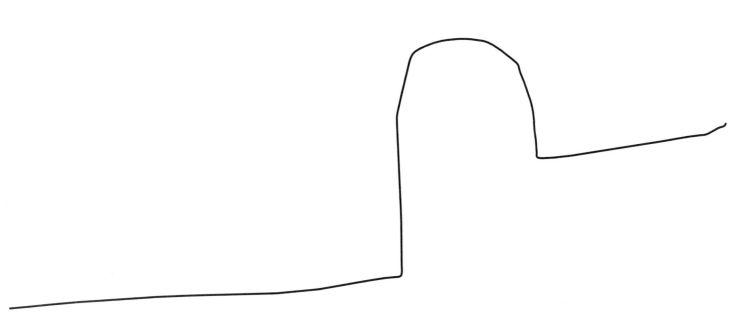

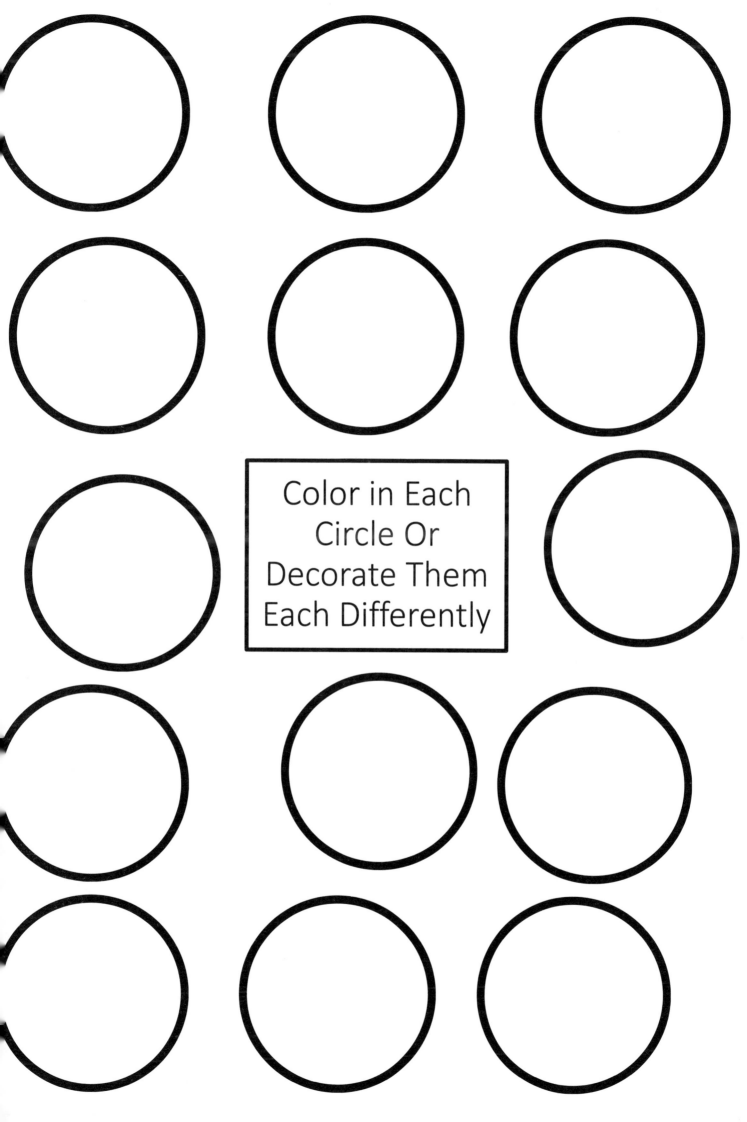

Color in Each Circle Or Decorate Them Each Differently

Grab a Rock, Paint it and Then Stamp it on This Page

Draw Your Dream House

Draw Your Favorite Breakfast Meal

This Square Needs To Be EXTRA

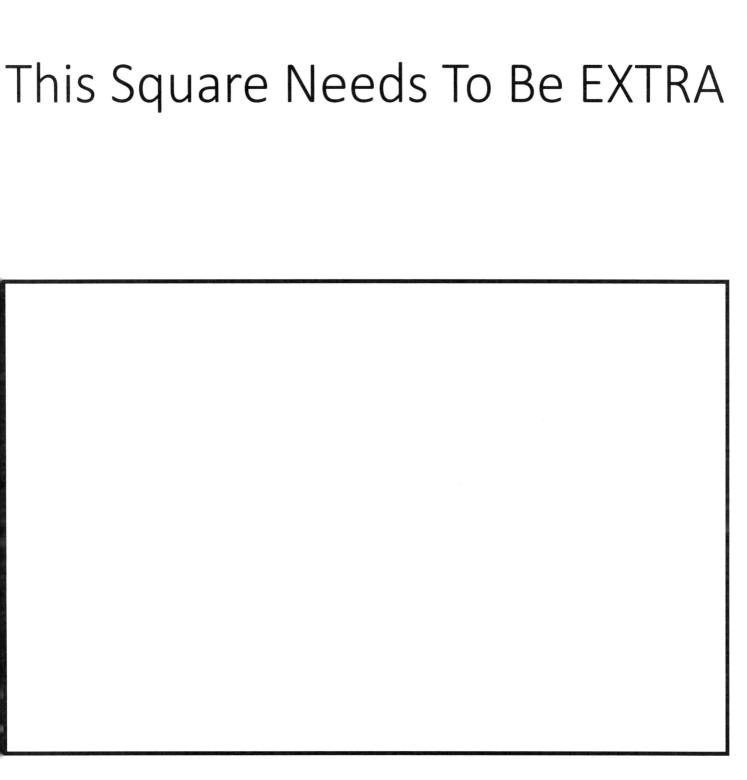

What's Your Idea

What's Your Favorite Season

Make Something Out of Aluminum Foil and Glue it Here